THE VIRTUE ALP...

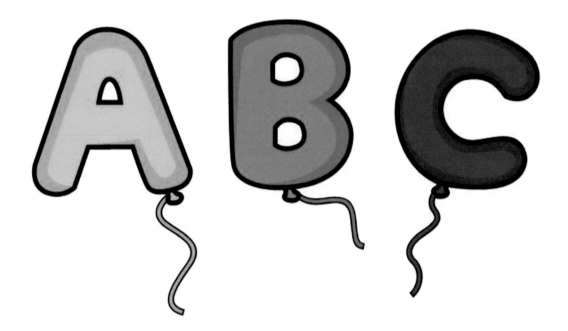

Written by Mona Adaba
Illustrations by Enig

This book is dedicated to my son Cayden, who reminds me that I can make a difference in the lives of all little ones. Thanks to my dear husband and wonderful family for all their love and support.

ISBN: 978-1-7330389-0-4

A: Active

Abel loves riding his bike. Abel is an active boy

B: Brave

Kelly does brave things.
Kelly can overcome fear.

C: Caring

Yvonne is caring to all who cross her path.

D: Disciplined

Ciara is disciplined and is careful to control her actions even when she is very excited.

E: Excellence

Cayden gives his best to every task.

F: Forgiveness

Olga and Lambert have learned
to forgive each other. They are very forgiving.

G: Generosity

Annie shares freely
without expecting a gift or reward in return.

H: Honesty

Richard is an honest boy.
He returns what doesn't belong to him.

I: Independent

Obinna can do things for himself.
Obinna is an independent boy.

J: Joy

Helen is always happy and singing.
Helen is filled with joy.

K: Kindness

Mikaela is kind to all around her.
She treats others the way she wishes to be treated.

L: Loving

The Brown family has allowed their hearts to burn with loving-kindness for all they meet.

M: Modest

Clarisse is very smart
and continually receives compliments.
Although she is highly praised,
she is always modest when she speaks or acts.

N: Noble

Fred does goodly acts. Fred is very noble.

O: Obedience

Hilda always listens to mommy.
Hilda is very obedient.

P: Patience

Alain is very patient.
Everything always works out for him at the end.

Q: Quiet

Elvis always takes time to
calm down and listen to his surroundings.

R: Respectful

Zola treats her parents very kindly.
Zola is very respectful.

S: Service

Harriette makes a point to assist those around her.
She is always of service.

T: Truthfulness

Mona always tells the truth. Truthfulness is the foundation of all human virtues.

U: Unity

We should celebrate our diversity
but always remember we remain
one single human race.

V: Virtuous

Charlene possesses qualities
that are morally good.

W: Wise

Bruce is very wise.
He always demonstrates good judgement.

X: eXpressive

Jeanine uses her words, writing, and gestures to convey meaning and emotion to others.

Y: Yearning

Jennifer yearns to be a good person in life.

Z: Zeal

Seth has a strong enthusiasm
for whatever he decides to do.

The End

57256039R00020

Made in the USA
Middletown, DE
28 July 2019